Ben Franklin
and His First Kite

written by
Stephen Krensky

illustrated by
Bert Dodson

Aladdin

New York   London   Toronto   Sydney   Singapore

First Aladdin edition June 2002

Aladdin Paperbacks

An imprint of Simon & Schuster

Children's Publishing Division

1230 Avenue of the Americas

New York, NY 10020

The text for this book was set in 18 Point Century Old Style.

Designed by Lisa Vega.

The illustrations were rendered in water color.

Manufactured in the United States of America

8 10 9

Library of Congress Cataloging-in-Publication Data:

Krensky, Stephen.

Ben Franklin and his first kite / written by Stephen Krensky ;

illustrated by Bert Dodson.–1st Aladdin ed.

p. cm.

Summary: Two popular series, Ready-to-Read and Childhood of Famous Americans, combine

to present the story of young Ben Franklin who loves doing experiments and cannot wait to

test out his latest idea involving a kite!

ISBN-13: 978-0-689-84984-8 (ISBN-10: 0-689-84984-2) (pbk.)

ISBN-13: 978-0-689-84985-5 (ISBN-10: 0-689-84985-0) (library ed.)

[1. Franklin, Benjamin, 1706-1790–Childhood and youth–Juvenile literature.

2. Franklin, Benjamin, 1706-1790–Childhood and youth. 3. Scientists–United States–

Biography–Juvenile literature. 4. Inventors–United States–Biography–Juvenile literature.

5. Scientists. 6. Inventors.]

[E]-dc21

2003273907

Ten-year-old Benjamin Franklin
was hard at work
in his father's candle shop.
He was cutting wicks.
He carefully laid out each one.

Ben stretched his arms
and let out a yawn.
Candles could be tall or short,
fat or thin,
and even different colors.
But there was nothing fun
about candles for Ben.

"When do you think
   we'll be done today?"
   Ben asked his father.
"Soon enough," his father answered.

"Why? Do you have special plans?"
Ben's father smiled.
It was a rare day indeed
when Ben did not have
a plan in mind.

"Yes," said Ben.

"I want to try an experiment
 at the millpond."

"You'll be swimming, then?"
 his father asked.

Ben grinned. "Partly," he said.

His father nodded.

Ben was a fine swimmer.

That afternoon Ben
flew down the streets of Boston.
He was headed for home.
Along the way he noticed the
waves cresting in the harbor.
The ships rocked back and forth.
That was good, he thought.
He needed a strong wind today.

11

When Ben got to his house,

his mother met him at the door.

Inside, two of his sisters

were busy making

hasty pudding by the hearth.

Ben had sixteen brothers and sisters.

"Ben," his mother said,

"why are you in such a hurry?"

Ben told her about his plan.

"Since your father approves,
I won't keep you,"
said his mother.
"Just be back for supper."
Ben nodded.
He ran to get the kite
he had made the week before.
Then he left the house.

At the millpond
a few of Ben's friends
had arrived to watch.
"You've picked a poor place
to fly a kite," said one.
Ben shrugged.
"I'm doing an experiment," he said.

Ben got undressed.

He gave his clothes

to one of his friends.

"Please carry these

to the other side

of the pond," he said.

"What are you going to do?"

asked the other boys.

"Carry the kite while you swim?"

"No," said Ben.

"The kite is going

to carry me."

"But that kite's nothing special.

It's just paper, sticks, and string,"

said one boy.

"That's true," Ben said.

"But you see,

the kite isn't the invention.

The invention is what

I'm going to do with it."

Ben raised the kite in the air.
Once the wind had caught
and carried it aloft,
Ben walked into the water.
There he lay on his back, floating.

"I'm going to cross this pond
without swimming a stroke,"
said Ben.

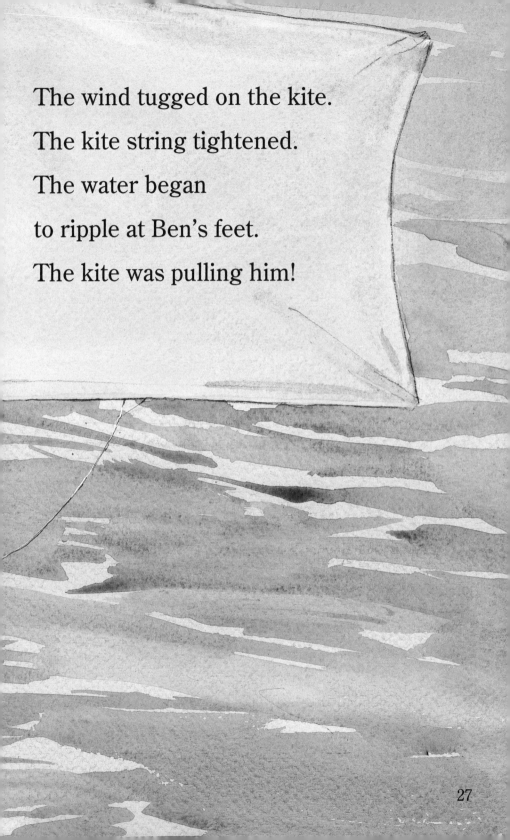

The wind tugged on the kite.

The kite string tightened.

The water began
to ripple at Ben's feet.

The kite was pulling him!

The boys whooped
and hollered as Ben
glided across the pond.
Finally he reached the other side.
The other boys met him there.
"That was amazing!" said one.
"You crossed the whole pond
    without swimming a stroke,"
    said another.

"What will you do next?"

they asked.

"Another invention?"

"A different experiment?"

Ben didn't know.

But he was sure he would think

of something.

This book is based on a story about Benjamin Franklin. The timeline below identifies important events in his life.

1706   Born on January 17, the fifteenth of seventeen children

1716   Goes to work in his father's chandlery at age 10

1718   Becomes apprentice to his brother James

1723   Runs away from Boston for Philadelphia

1729   Buys the *Pennsylvania Gazette*

1730   Marries Deborah Read (has three children)

1732   Begins to print *Poor Richard's Almanack*

1740   Invents Pennsylvania fireplace, later called Franklin Stove

1752   Flies kite in thunderstorm to show that lightning is a form of electricity

1775   Joins the Second Continental Congress

1776   Helps draft and signs the *Declaration of Independence*

1776   Becomes American representative to France

1783   Helps negotiate Treaty of Paris

1790   Dies in Philadelphia on April 17